S0-AZX-510

Science Where You Go

Mc Graw Hill **Wright Group**

The McGraw-Hill Companies

Art Credits: ©The McGraw-Hill Companies, Inc. would like to thank the following illustrators for their contributions: Scott Pearson, Durga Bernhard.

Photo Credits: Cover front ©Johner/Getty Images; **4** ©Sam Cornwell/Shutterstock Images LLC; **5** (tl) ©Christopher Elwell/Shutterstock Images LLC; (tr) ©Brand X images; (bl) ©Garry Wade/Getty Images; (br) ©Marvin E. Newman/Getty Images; **6** ©Xtuv Photography/ Shutterstock Images LLC; **7** ©The Granger Collection, New York; **8** AbleStock.com/ Jupiterimages; **9** ©Donovan Reese/Getty Images; **10** ©The Granger Collection, New York; **11** (t) ©Ingram Publishing/ SuperStock; (b) ©Santokh Kochar/Getty Images; **12** ©Museum of the City of New York/Corbis; **13** ©Kristian Cabanis/ Photolibrary; **14** ©Underwood & Underwood/Corbis; **15** ©The Granger Collection, New York; **16** ©Sam Cornwell/ Shutterstock Images LLC; **17** ©The Granger Collection, New York; **18** (l) ©Bettmann/Corbis; (r) ©Getty Images; **19** ©Charles E. Rotkin/Corbis; **20** ©Chris Kerrigan; **21** ©Gorin/Shutterstock Images LLC; **23** (l) ©SecondShot/ Shutterstock Images LLC; (r) ©Feraru Nicolae/Shuttestock Images LLC; **23** (l) ©SecondShot/Shutterstock Images LLC;

24 ©Charles E. Rotkin/Corbis; **25** (t) ©Ron Levine/Getty Images; (c) ©Punchstock; (b) ©Andy Crawford/Getty Images; **61** (t) ©Marvin E. Newman/Getty Images; **61** (c) ©Mike Brinson/Getty Images; (b) ©Image 100; **62** ©Johner /Getty Images; **63** ©Photos.com/Jupiterimages; **64** ©Olivier Le Queinec/Shutterstock Images LLC; **65** Courtesy of The New York Public Library.www.nypl.org; **66** (t) ©Jupiterimages; **66-67** ©Corbis; **67** (t) ©Stockxpert/Jupiterimages; **68** ©Stockxpert/Jupiterimages; **69** ©The Granger Collection, New York; **70** ©The McGraw-Hill Companies, Inc./Lars A. Niki, photographer; **71** ©Mark Henley/Photolibrary; **72** ©Wolfgang Kaehler/Corbis; **73** ©Digital Vision/Stockdisc; **74** ©Kim Karpeles/Age Fotostock; **75** ©Alan Copson/ Photolibrary; **76-77** ©Royalty Free/Corbis; **77** ©Peter Carroll/ Photolibrary; **78-79** (t) ©Holger Mette /Shutterstock Images LLC; **80** ©Stockxpert/Jupiterimages; **81** ©Holger Mette / Shuttrstock Images LLC; **86** (t) ©Chris Kerrigan; (b) ©Stockxpert/Jupiterimages; **87** ©Royalty Free/Corbis.

www.WrightGroup.com

Wright Group

Copyright © 2011 by The McGraw-Hill Companies, Inc.

All rights reserved. Except as permitted under the United States Copyright Act, no part of this publication may be reproduced or distributed in any form or by any means, or stored in a database or retrieval system, without the prior written permission from the publisher, unless otherwise indicated.

Printed in China.

Send all inquiries to:
Wright Group/McGraw-Hill
P.O. Box 812960
Chicago, IL 60681

ISBN 978-007-656740-9
MHID 0-07-656740-0

4 5 6 7 8 9 DSS 16 15 14 13 12 11

Contents

Digital 21

My Home Page   ebook   online coach

How is science a part of our community?

Where can we see science around us? Workers use tools and technology to help in their jobs. We use science to understand and take care of nature in our community, and to travel quickly and safely. Science is at work all around.

Focus Questions

Selection ❶

How are communities built?

Selection ❷

How do people in the community use tools and technology?

Selection ❸

How is nature a part of our community?

Selection ❹

How does science help us get around the community?

Preview   online coach

How are communities built? Preview pages 6–23. Then read *Touching the Sky* to find out.

Touching the Sky

the Sky

By Jane Kelley

Chapter 1
Living and Working Together

Cities are places where many people live.
Most cities started small.
They grew bigger as more people
moved to them.

These people needed places
to live and work.
But cities couldn't keep <u>spreading</u> out.
People began to build up **instead**.

spreading: growing

In the 1880s the buildings
were not very tall.

How do you make a tall building?
Builders thought about using wood.
But wood isn't very strong.
Builders had to make new **plans**.

Low apartment buildings
can be made using wood.

Builders tried using stones instead.
Stones are strong.
But they are also very heavy.
They didn't work well
for tall buildings either.

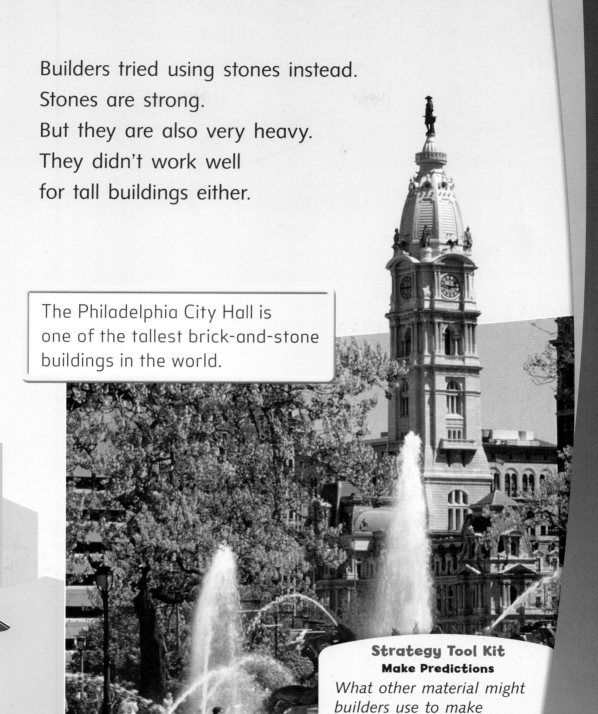

The Philadelphia City Hall is one of the tallest brick-and-stone buildings in the world.

Strategy Tool Kit
Make Predictions
What other material might builders use to make a tall building?

9

Using Steel

Steel is a metal.
In the 1850s people discovered
how to make steel **cheaply**.

discovered: learned

Melted steel is made
into useful shapes.

Steel is strong and hard.
It can be changed into different shapes.
Thin **pieces** of steel are lighter
than large blocks of stone.
Steel is good for making tall buildings.

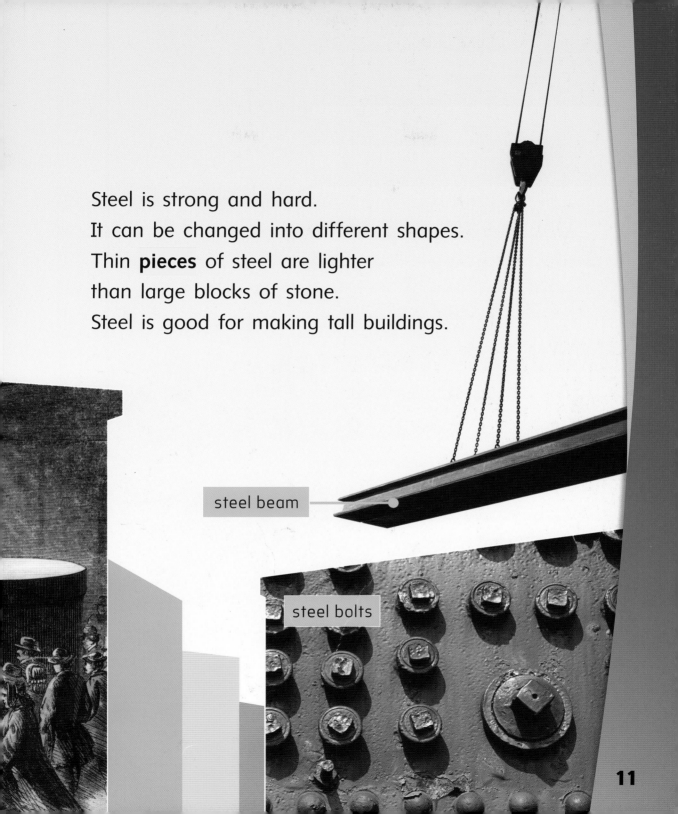

steel beam

steel bolts

Builders used steel to make tall frames.
The frames went up the <u>middle</u>
of the buildings.
They held the buildings up
from the inside.

middle: inside

girder

Builders used steel girders
for the Woolworth Building
in New York City.

Now, the support was on the inside.
The outside walls could be thin.
They could even be made from glass.

The Flatiron Building
in New York City was
one of the first buildings
made using a steel skeleton.

What was it like to see the first tall buildings?
They looked like they touched the sky.
People called them skyscrapers.

Offices, stores, and hotels are in skyscrapers.
People can live in skyscrapers too.

The Home Insurance Building was built in Chicago in 1885. The frame in this building was iron, not steel.

The Empire State Building in New York City is 102 stories tall. For almost 40 years it was the world's tallest building.

Stop and Think
Why was the discovery of steel important?

Chapter 3
Going Up?

Climbing to the top of tall buildings
is hard work!

When tall buildings were first made,
builders put in **elevators**
to take people up and down.
But they weren't very safe.
People were afraid to use them.

afraid: scared

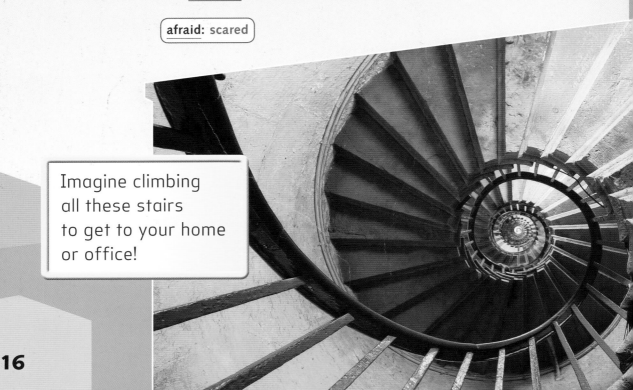

Imagine climbing
all these stairs
to get to your home
or office!

Early elevators often had people to open and close the doors and select the floors for passengers.

Elisha Otis found a way
to make elevators safe.
He added **brakes** to them.
The brakes would <u>keep</u>
the elevators from falling.

keep: stop

Elisha Otis

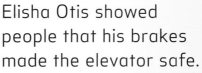

Elisha Otis showed
people that his brakes
made the elevator safe.

18

Soon many buildings had elevators.
It was now easy for people to get to the top.
Buildings got taller and taller.

By the mid-1900s New York City
was crowded with skyscrapers.

Strategy Tool Kit
Ask and Answer Questions
*Why would buildings
need to be taller and taller?*

19

Chapter 4
How High Can We Go?

Today lots of people live in cities.
Many of them live in skyscrapers.
But people don't want
too many tall buildings.

Very tall skyscrapers have space
for many families to live.

Tall buildings block sunlight.
Cities have made rules about
how many skyscrapers can be built.

In many places tall buildings
are not allowed.
This apartment building is
only four stories high.

Builders now have better **technology**.
They can make different kinds
of tall buildings.
They can build round skyscrapers.
They can build skyscrapers 110 **stories** high!

People still want to build higher and higher.
How high do you think we will go?

Skyscrapers around the World

Empire State Building, New York City, United States	Petronas Towers, Kuala Lumpur, Malaysia	World Financial Center, Shanghai, China	Taipei 101, Taipei, China	Burj Khalifa, United Arab Emirates
1,250 feet	1,483 feet	1,614 feet	1,677 feet	2,680+ feet

These modern skyscrapers are interesting shapes.

Burj Khalifa, United Arab Emirates

Turning Torso, Sweden

Focus Question
How are communities built?

A ## Check Understanding ★

What important things did you learn about building a community from reading this selection? Write your ideas. PRACTICE COMPANION **85**

B ## Understand Text Features ★★

In nonfiction texts, labels are sometimes used to show the names of things in photographs. Find a photograph with a label. How does the label help you? Discuss with a partner.

C ## Think Critically ★★★★

How is science a part of our community? Discuss this with your group.

My Home Page

Focus Question

How do people in the community use tools and technology?

Show What You Know

Have you ever seen community workers using special tools or technology? Write down what you saw.

PRACTICE COMPANION **86**

 online coach

How do people in the community use tools and technology? Preview pages 26–41. Then read *The Wobbly Tooth* to find out.

The Wobbly Tooth

By Lizzie Stace

Illustrated by Scott Pearson

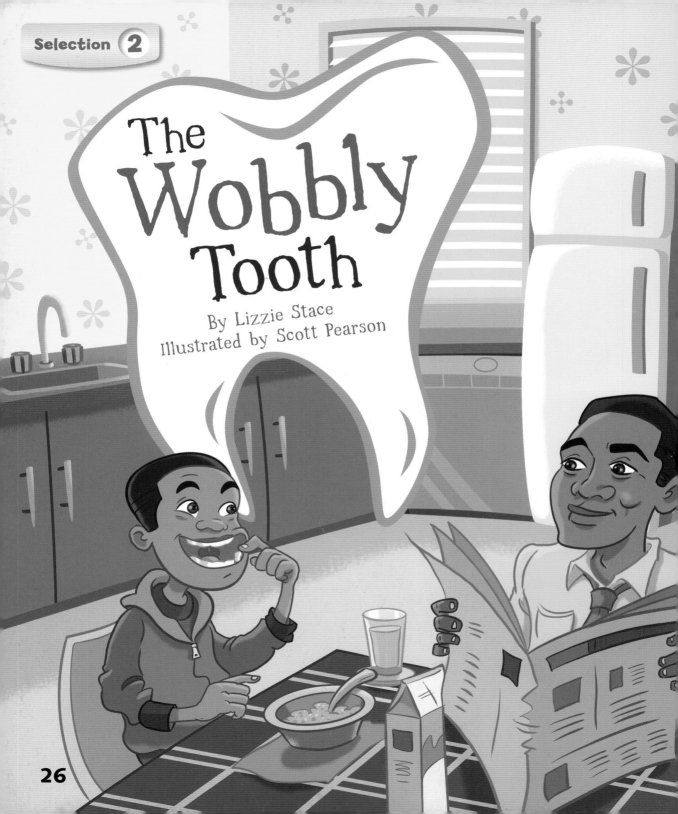

Chapter One
Eli's Wobbly Tooth

Eli woke up.
One of his front teeth felt strange.
He pushed his **tongue** against it.
The tooth moved.

"I've got a wobbly tooth!" thought Eli.

At breakfast he showed his dad.

"It's time for your tooth
to come out," said Eli's dad.
"Then a new one can grow."

wobbly: moving

"Maybe it will come out if I wobble it,"
thought Eli.

All that day, Eli kept wobbling his tooth.
He wobbled it from side to side.
He wobbled it around and around.

He wobbled and wobbled it,
but the tooth would not come out.

It was **starting** to hurt from all that wobbling.

Strategy Tool Kit
Make Connections
What does a wobbly tooth feel like?

Chapter Two — Eli Asks for Help

Eli asked his <u>friend</u> Otis what to do.

"Eat an apple," said Otis.
"When you chomp down,
your tooth will come out in the apple!"

So Eli ate an apple.
Then he ate **another** apple.
And another.
Soon Eli was sick of apples.

But the tooth didn't come out.

friend: buddy

Eli asked his friend Abby what to do.

"Just wait," said Abby.
"Your tooth will come out at night.
One morning you will find it on your pillow."

So Eli waited three nights.

But each morning, there was no tooth on his pillow.

Eli's mom decided it was time to go to the **dentist**.

Stop and Think
How have people tried to help Eli?

33

Chapter Three

Going to the Dentist

Eli lay in the big chair at the dentist's <u>office</u>.

"Will this hurt?" Eli asked.

Eli's mom shook her head.
"The dentist will know just what to do,"
she said.

office: room

Eli pointed at the X-ray machine.
"What's that?" he asked.

"Pretty cool machine, isn't it?"
said the dentist.
"That machine takes
pictures inside your mouth."

The dentist showed Eli the mirror she used
to look inside his mouth.
Eli could see his tonsils.

"Wow!" he said.
"This is very cool!"

The dentist showed Eli the tool
she used to check for **cavities**.

She turned on a **bright** light.

"This helps me see inside your mouth,"
she said.

Strategy Tool Kit
Make Predictions
What do you think will happen to Eli's tooth?

37

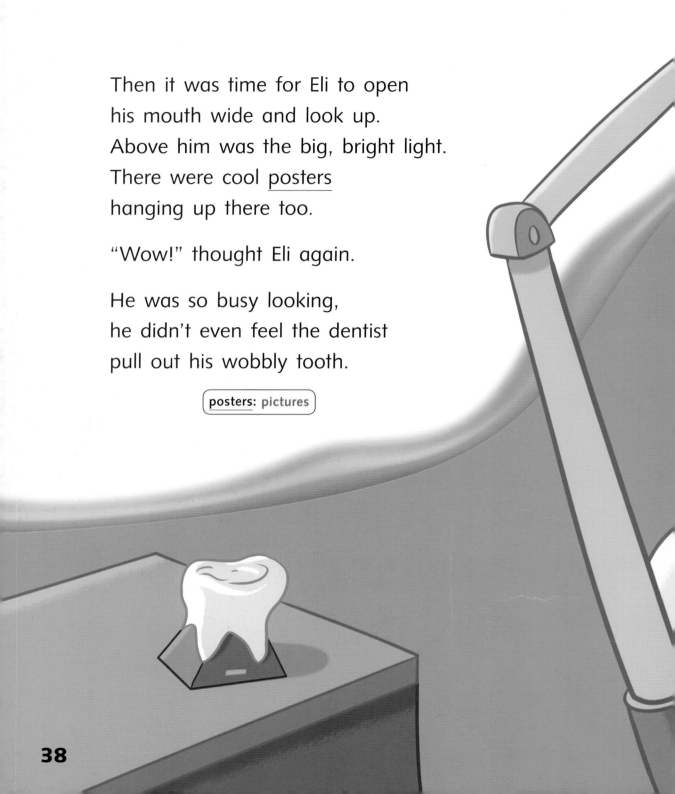

Then it was time for Eli to open
his mouth wide and look up.
Above him was the big, bright light.
There were cool <u>posters</u>
hanging up there too.

"Wow!" thought Eli again.

He was so busy looking,
he didn't even feel the dentist
pull out his wobbly tooth.

posters: pictures

38

Back in school Eli showed
Otis and Abby his new **gap**.

"I told you that eating an apple would work,"
said Otis.

"But it came out at night, didn't it?"
asked Abby.

Eli shook his head
and smiled his new, gappy smile.

"The dentist pulled it out," he said.
"And it didn't hurt one bit."

Focus Question
How do people in the community use tools and technology?

A ## Check Understanding ★

What special tools or technology did the worker in this story use to help her do her job? How did they make her job easier? Write your ideas.

PRACTICE COMPANION **97**

B ## Understand Literary Elements ★★

Think about the main characters in this story. How do they talk and act with each other? What does this tell you about them? Share with your partner.

C ## Think Critically ★★★★

How is science a part of our community? Talk about this with the group.

My Home Page

Focus Question

How is nature a part of our community?

★★★★

Show What You Know

What plants or animals have you seen in your community? Where did you see them? Discuss with the group.

PRACTICE COMPANION 98

 Preview

How is nature a part of our community? Preview pages 44–59. Then read *Rosa's Diary* to find out.

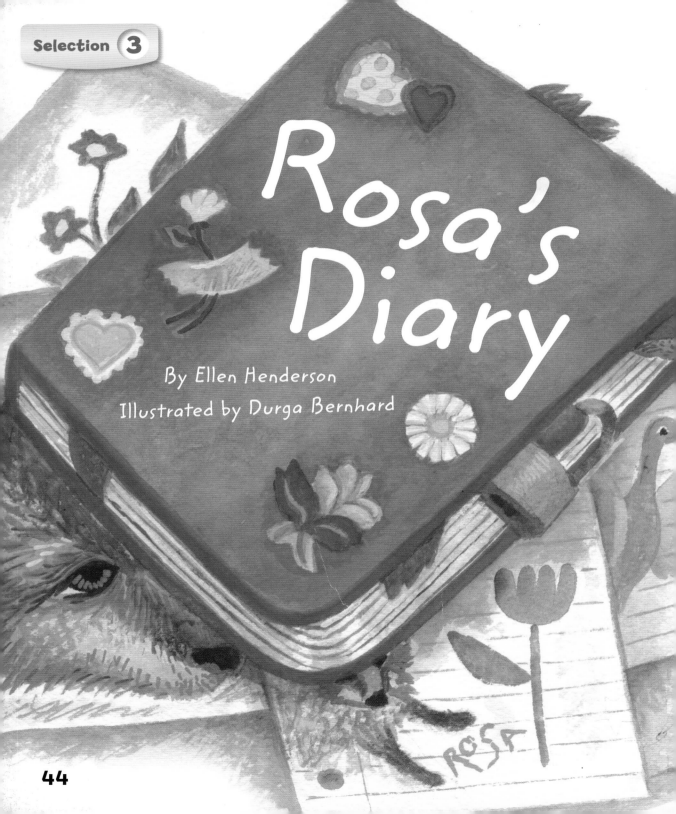

Rosa's Diary

By Ellen Henderson

Illustrated by Durga Bernhard

Chapter One
Rosa Sees the Foxes

Sunday

Today I saw three foxes!

I saw a mother fox and her two kits.
They all had **bushy** tails and pointy ears.

The foxes were in our yard.
They were <u>sniffing</u> our garbage can.

My brother Eddie saw them too.
He was so excited that he started yelling.

> sniffing: smelling

The garbage lid fell,
and the foxes ran away.
They were very fast.
I couldn't see where
they went.

Then Dad came back
from his run.
He told us that foxes don't
often come near people.
They live in the woods.

I wondered why the foxes
had come to our yard.

Chapter Two

Rosa Finds Out about Foxes

Monday

I went to the **library** to find out
more about foxes.
Eddie helped me look for books.

I found out that there are
different kinds of foxes.
The ones in our yard are red foxes.

Red foxes eat mice.
They also eat birds and fruit.
In fact, they eat pretty much any food.

Strategy Tool Kit
Summarize
What has Rosa learned about foxes?

49

I read that foxes live
in meadows and woods.
But sometimes woods are cut down.
Streams become polluted.

Foxes **leave** their homes
to look for new places to live.
That's when they come near people.

Dad says the woods near us
have just been cut down.
That's why the foxes were in our yard.

Stop and Think
*Why might foxes look
for new homes?*

Chapter Three

Mom Fox Wrecks the Yard

Tuesday

This morning I watched the mom fox
with Dad's **binoculars**.

Eddie wanted a turn too.
He was so excited,
he nearly dropped Dad's binoculars!

The mom fox had <u>tipped</u>
the garbage can over.
Lots of garbage had spilled out.

She was digging a hole in our yard.
Dad says she might be digging a **den**.

tipped: pushed

53

Dad says the foxes are **wrecking** our yard.
They need to be caught and moved.
He **cleaned** up the yard.
Then he called the animal-control officer.

Eddie started to cry.
I gave him a hug.
I felt sad too, but I knew Dad was right.
The foxes need a home of their own.

Chapter Four
Catching the Foxes

Friday

The animal-control officer
had a clever plan.
He put a trap in our yard.
He put food in the trap for two nights.
But he didn't set the trap.
Both nights the food was gone.

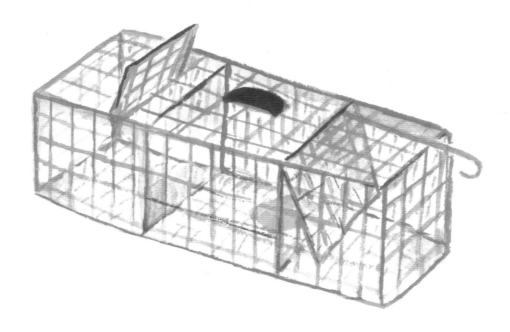

Last night he set the trap.
The door shut behind the mom fox.

Strategy Tool Kit
Summarize
How did the animal-control officer plan to catch the foxes?

57

The animal-control officer
caught the kits too.
He is taking the foxes to
a wildlife **reserve**.
The reserve is a good home for foxes.
The trees there won't be cut down.

I'm sad our foxes are going.
But I'm happy they will be in a place
where they can be safe.

Chapter 1
The First Trains

Trains carry people and things
from place to place.
Trains move along railway tracks.

The first trains were
made in England.
They could not go
very fast or far.
But they were able
to <u>carry</u> heavy things.

carry: move

George Stephenson built
one of the first steam trains.
It was called *Rocket*.

The first trains used steam engines.
Steam engines burn coal.
They give off a lot of smoke.

Smoke pours out
of this steam engine.

New technology was **invented**.
Engines began using
diesel and electric power.
Trains now put less **pollution** into the air.
They also became quieter and faster.

diesel: oil

Electric engines like this one
were also cheaper to run.

Strategy Tool Kit
Summarize
How were new trains different from the first trains?

More and more people
began using trains.
Train travel was faster than walking.
It was faster than riding a horse.
One train could carry
many people at a time.
Trains could carry heavy things too.

travel: riding

This passenger train
in Sweden runs on electricity.

Today we have different ways to travel.
But we still use trains.

Chicago railroad yards, 1909

Chapter 2
Going Under

Some train tracks are built inside tunnels.
The tunnels are under the ground.
Underground trains are often
called **subway** trains.

Subway trains
can travel very fast.

This drawing from the 1860s shows Baker Street Station in London, England.

The first subway opened in 1863.
It was in London, England.
The first subway in the United States
was built in Boston.
It opened in 1897.

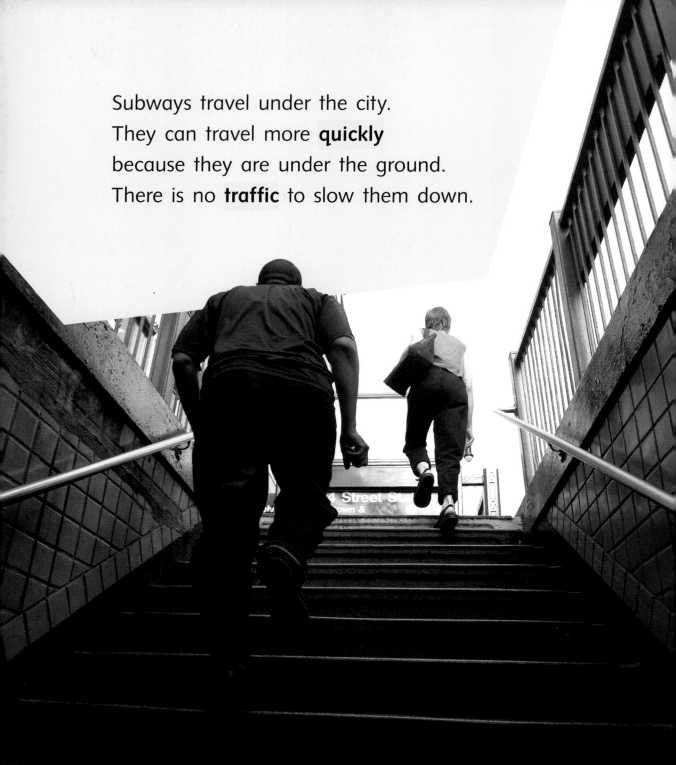

Subways travel under the city.
They can travel more **quickly**
because they are under the ground.
There is no **traffic** to slow them down.

People can read books
or do work on subways.
They can keep warm and dry
when the weather is bad.

Stop and Think
Why do many people still use trains?

71

Some trains go through mountains.
Building a tunnel through a mountain
takes a lot of **planning**.

Builders must decide on
the best path to build a tunnel
through a mountain.

tunnel

Other trains go under rivers.
Some even go under the ocean.
Trains can go almost anywhere.

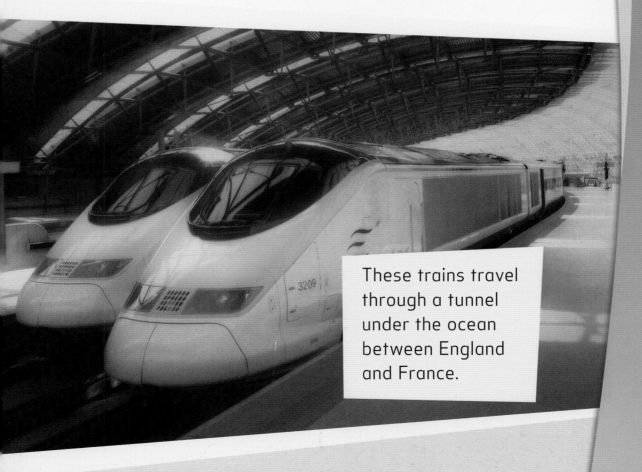

These trains travel through a tunnel under the ocean between England and France.

Chapter 3
Up and Over

Some trains run on tracks
that are raised in the air.
They don't take up space on the roads.
Traffic can still move under the train.

Chicago has a train that runs
on tracks raised above the ground.

This elevated train travels
above the traffic.

The "L"

Chicago's transportation system has trains that run aboveground, underground, and on the ground. Trains that are elevated run in a loop around the city. The "L" began in 1892, and today some routes run 24 hours a day.

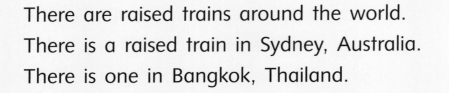

There are raised trains around the world.
There is a raised train in Sydney, Australia.
There is one in Bangkok, Thailand.

Both those trains are monorails.
They run on one rail, not two.
Most monorails run on electricity.
They don't pollute the air.

The monorail
in Sydney, Australia,
travels in a loop
around the city.

Sightseeing

People like to sightsee
from raised trains.
People who visit this park
in Orlando, Florida, can see
the sights of the park
from a monorail.
It is almost 15 miles long—
one of the longest in the world.

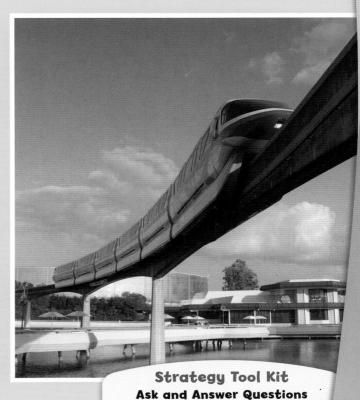

Strategy Tool Kit
Ask and Answer Questions
*Why might cities have
raised trains?*

77

Chapter 4
Trains Today

Technology is always changing.
New technology makes
train travel even better.

One new idea is the maglev train.
The maglev train has no wheels.
Instead, it floats above big **magnets**.
It can travel up to 310 miles an hour!
That is very fast.

Scale Diagram of a Maglev Train

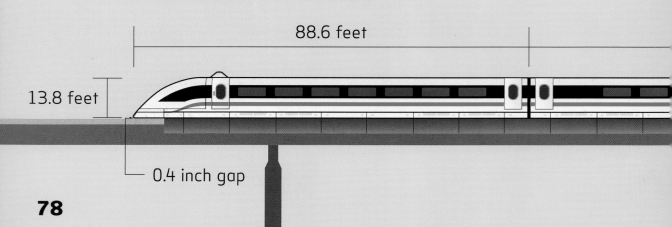

88.6 feet

13.8 feet

0.4 inch gap

78

This maglev train is in Shanghai, China. It can travel almost 19 miles in less than 8 minutes.

81.4 feet 88.6 feet

Trains are an important kind of **transportation**.
They connect our communities.
They take us many places.

Focus Question
How does science help us
get around the community?

A **Check Understanding** ★

What things in this selection make getting around
easier? If those things were gone, how would
communities change? Write your ideas.

PRACTICE COMPANION **136**

B **Understand Text Features** ★★

A scale diagram is a small drawing of a large
object. Look at the diagram of the train on
pages 78–79. What does the diagram tell you
about the train?

C **Think Critically** ★★★★

How is science a part of our community?
Talk about this with the group.

My Home
Page

Respond to the THEME Question

How is science a part of our community?

Use these activities to show what you've learned about the theme question.

Design and Create

1. Think of a new tool to help a community worker.

2. Sketch the tool and label each part.

3. Write a paragraph to explain how your tool will make the job easier.

Multimedia

1. Choose a way science helps us get around.

2. Create a poster with text and diagrams.

3. Use the poster to share your ideas.

Book Club

1. Choose a topic from this unit that interests you.

2. Make a list of questions and research them in the library.

3. Share your information with the group.

Be an Author

1. Think about the fictional characters in this unit. How did they see science in their community?

2. Write your own short story. How do your characters see science in their community?

3. Read your writing to the class.

My Home Page

Glossary

another *adj.* one more;
He picked up the papers, and then he saw another paper under the chair. **30**

binoculars *n.*
something you look through to make faraway things seem closer;
She watched the birds through her binoculars. **52**

brakes *n.* things that slow something down;
He put on the brakes as he rode downhill. **18**

bright *adj.* shining strongly;
The sunlight was bright, so they wore sunglasses. **36**

bushy *adj.* thick and fluffed up, like a bush;
His dad had a bushy mustache. **45**

cavities *n.* small holes in a person's teeth caused by decay;
He had three cavities because he didn't brush his teeth every night. **36**

cheaply *adv.* in a way that costs less than usual;
She bought the books cheaply at a yard sale. **10**

cleaned *v.* made free from dirt or mess;
He cleaned the mud from his shoes before coming in. **54**

den *n.* a place where a wild animal keeps safe;
The wolf built a den for its pups. **53**

dentist *n.* a person who takes care of people's teeth;

The dentist put a filling in the child's sore tooth. **33**

elevators *n.* machines like boxes that carry people up and down a building;
They took the elevators instead of walking up the stairs. **16**

gap *n.* a space between two things;
There was a gap in the fence that she could look through. **40**

instead *adv.* in place of;
They went to the park instead of the mall. **7**

invented *v.* thought up;
He invented a new kind of bike. **65**

leave *v.* to go away;
They had to leave the party by nine o'clock. **51**

library *n.* a place where books are kept for people to borrow;
She finished her book, so she returned it to the library. **48**

magnets *n.* kinds of metal that stick to or push away other pieces of metal;
The nails stuck to the magnets. **78**

pieces *n.* bits;
The glass broke into many pieces. **11**

planning *v.* thinking and figuring out what to do;
The class was planning the best way to get to the zoo. **72**

plans *n.* drawings or diagrams that show where things go; The builder checked the plans before starting to work. **8**

pollution *n.* something that harms and dirties the environment; People found it hard to breathe because of the pollution in the air. **65**

quickly *adv.* in less time than usual; He quickly ran home from school to play with his friends. **70**

reserve *n.* a special park that is kept natural; The birds made their nests in the reserve because it was far away from the city. **58**

starting *v.* beginning; The weather had been sunny, but now it was starting to rain. **29**

stories *n.* levels of a building; A building with 20 stories is very tall. **22**

streams *n.* small rivers; Animals went to the streams to get water. **50**

subway *n.* an underground tunnel; They walked down the stairs to the subway. **68**

technology *n.* the tools and machines that help people do their jobs well; They used the best technology for building the house. **22**

tongue *n.* the soft part of the mouth that is used for tasting, licking, and talking;
The dog used its tongue to drink water. **27**

traffic *n.* cars, buses, and other vehicles that are on a road at the same time;
He was late for school because there was so much traffic. **70**

transportation *n.* the ways of moving people from place to place;

Trains are one kind of transportation in the city. **80**

wrecking *v.* messing up;
Her huge dog was wrecking the sofa with its claws. **54**

Index